AN EXPRESS BOOKS PUBLICATION

Printed by Eyre & Spottiswoode, Cosham, Hants. & co-ordinated by Roeder Print Services Ltd.

Welcome to Book Seven.

Seven years – sigh! Remember those days? Petrol was three farthings a gallon, cigarettes were tuppence a thousand and Britain used to occasionally win things at sport. My Doris was a petite size 24 and Dennis hit an intellectual peak with a brain-cell count of eleven.

And what of my two chroniclers, artist Andrew Christine and writer Roger Kettle?

Well, Andrew was a still-active 83 and Roger could still eat his meals without a straw. Anyway, enough nostalgia – I hope you enjoy this latest collection.

Love,

Beau Beep.

P.S. Hands up who said "I've been given a book of his every year for seven years but I don't remember breaking a mirror."?

THE ADVENTURES OF LEGIONNAIRE
BEAU PEEP

FROM **THE STAR**

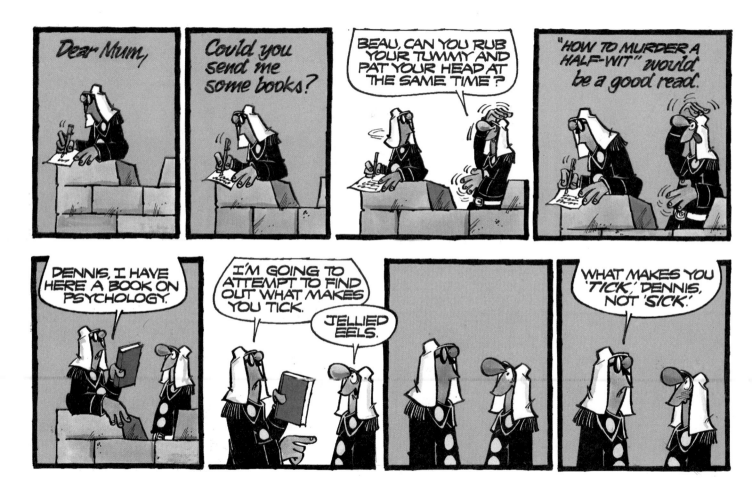

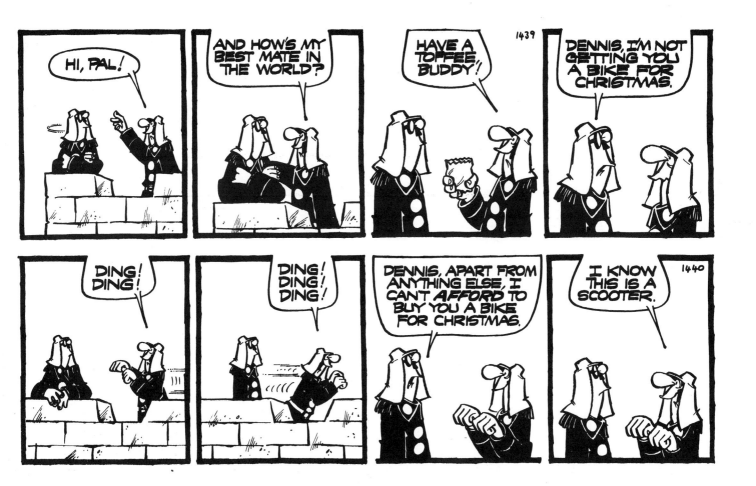

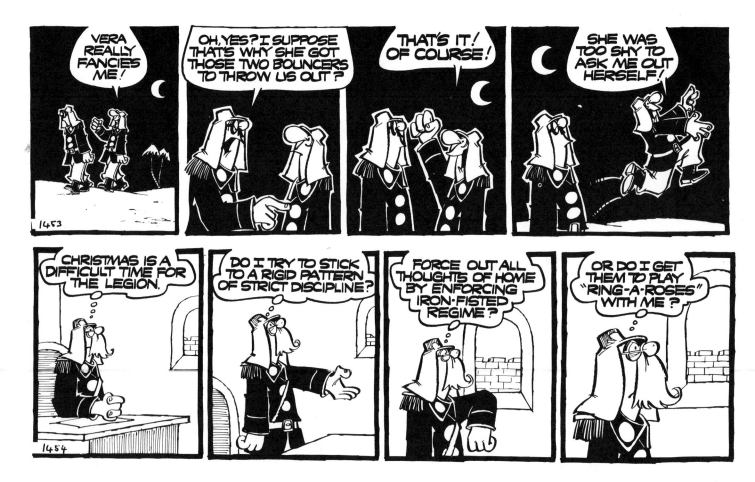

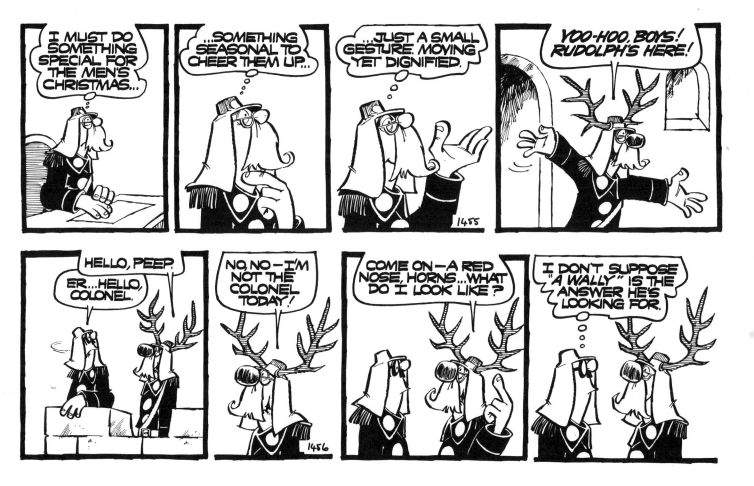

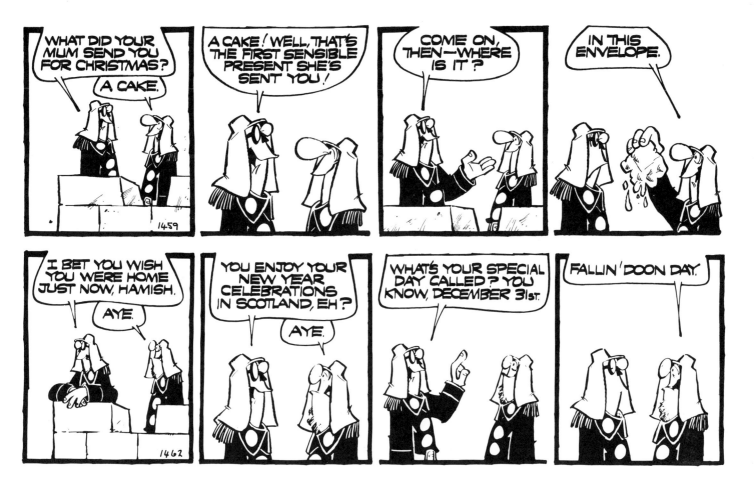

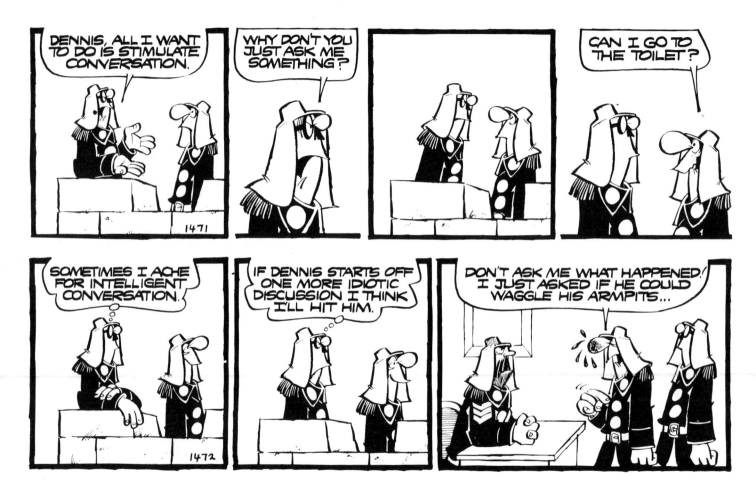

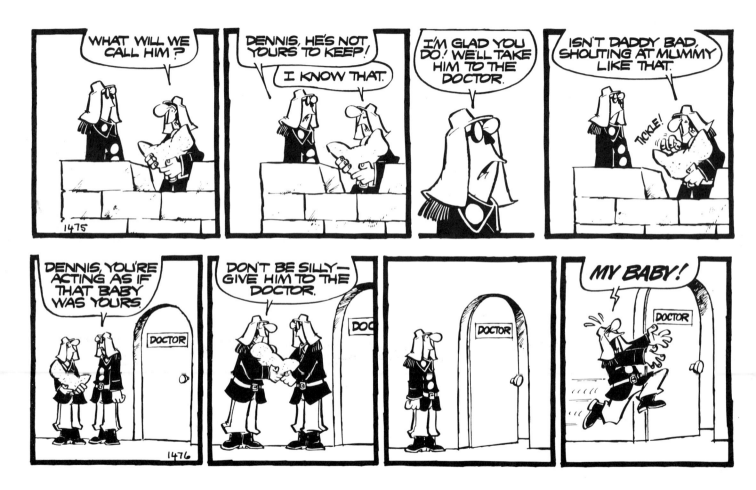

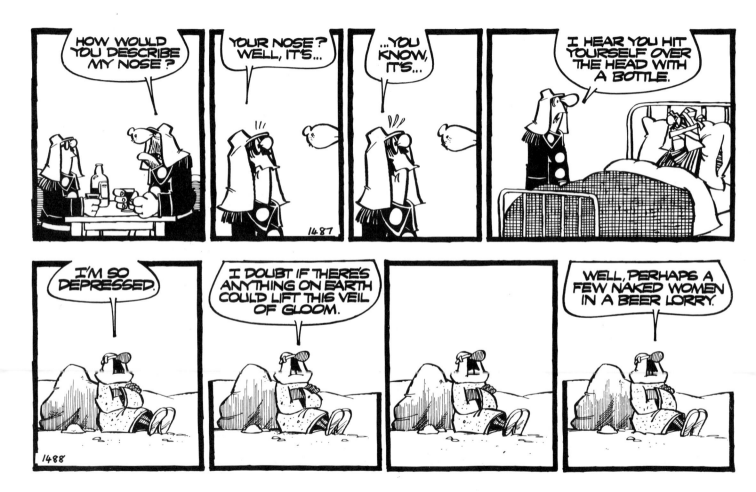

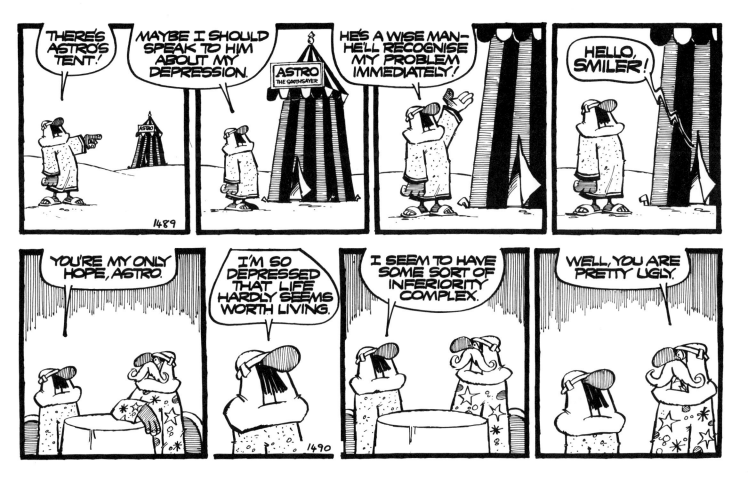

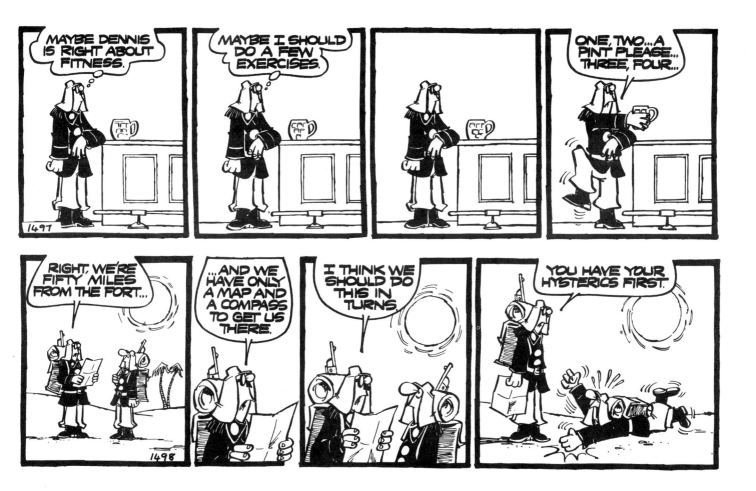

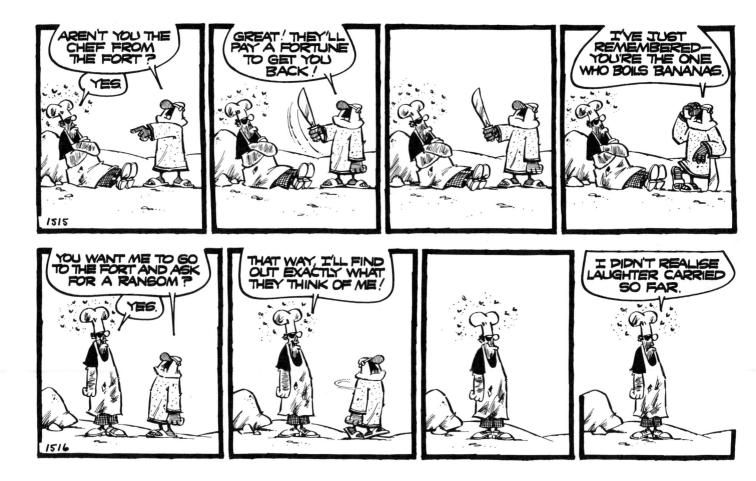

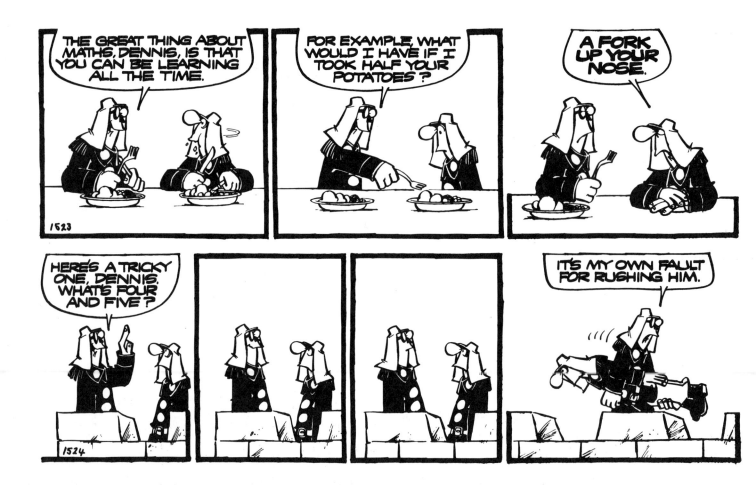

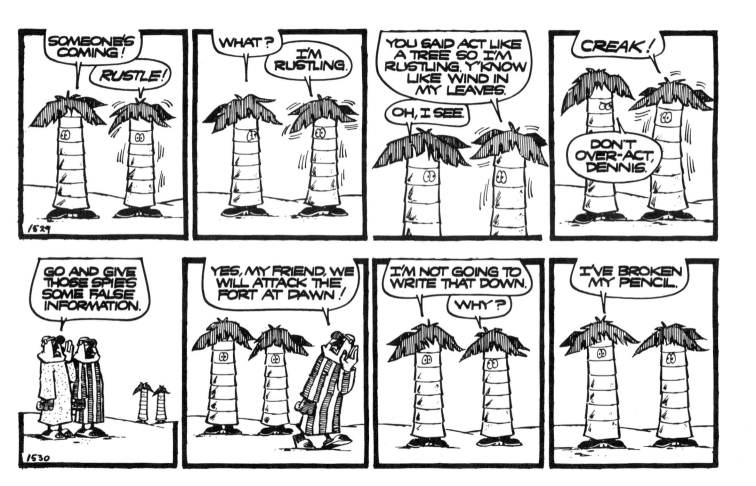

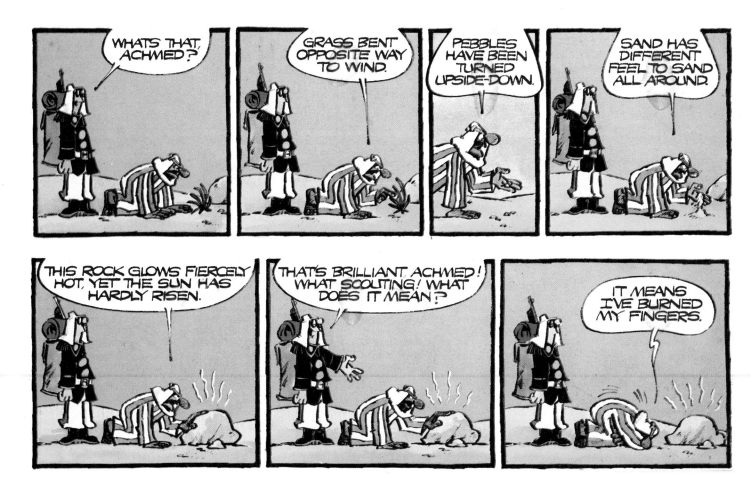

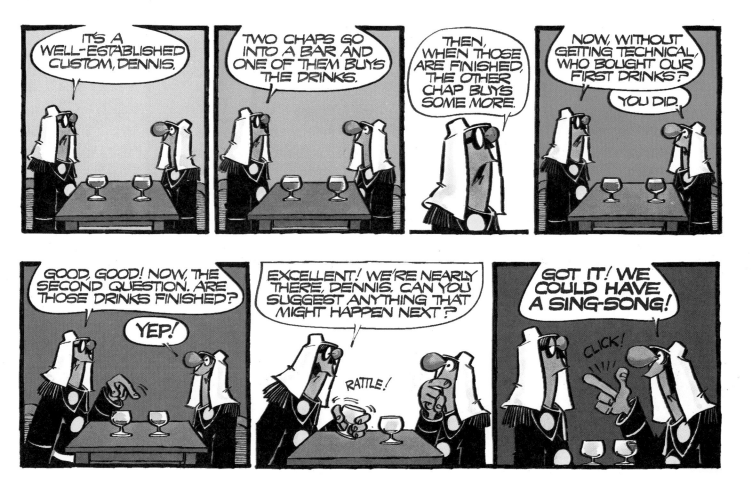

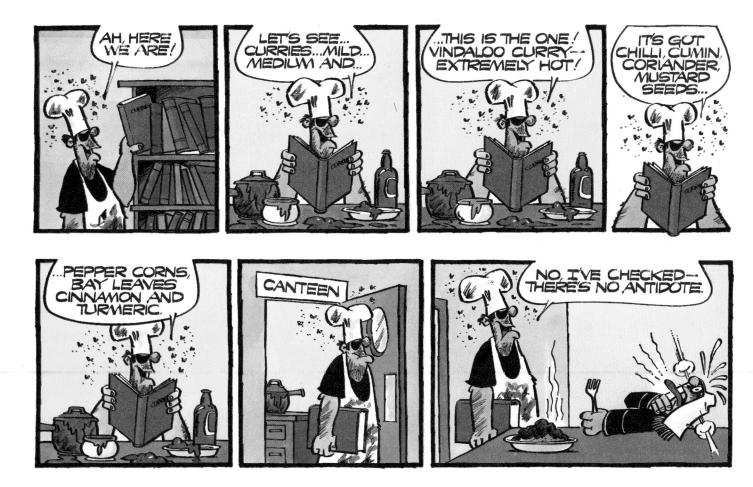

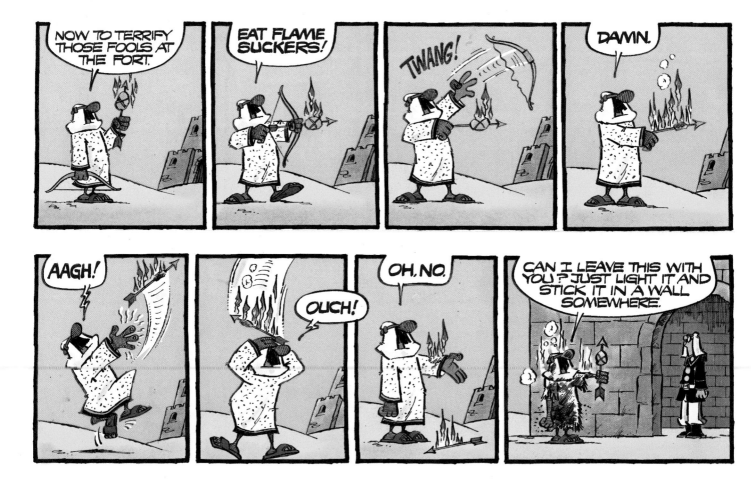

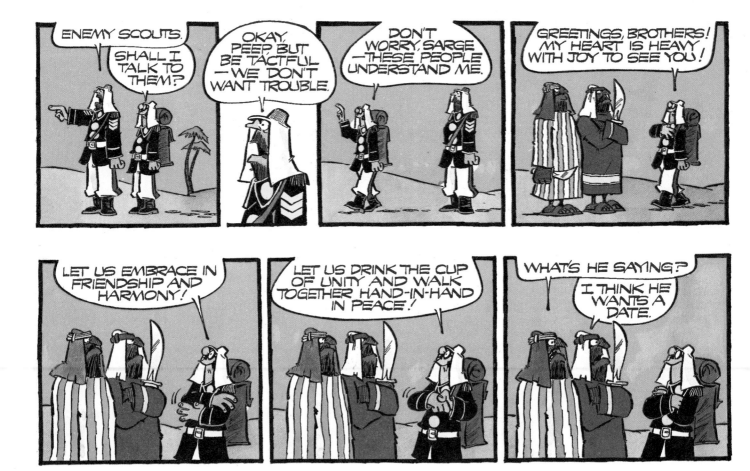

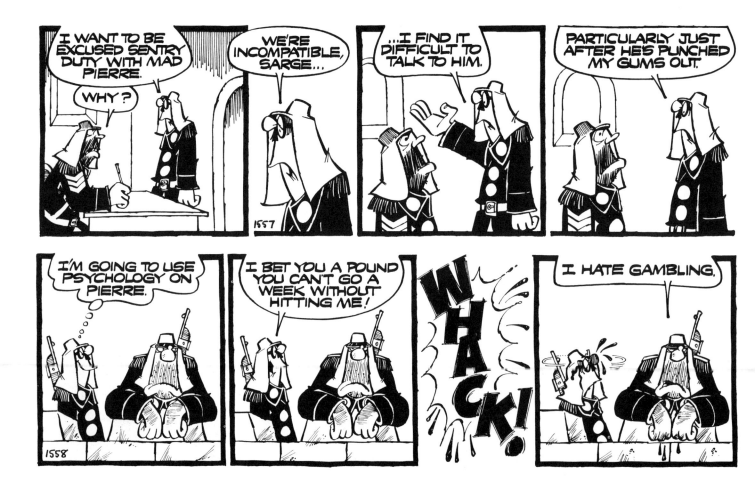

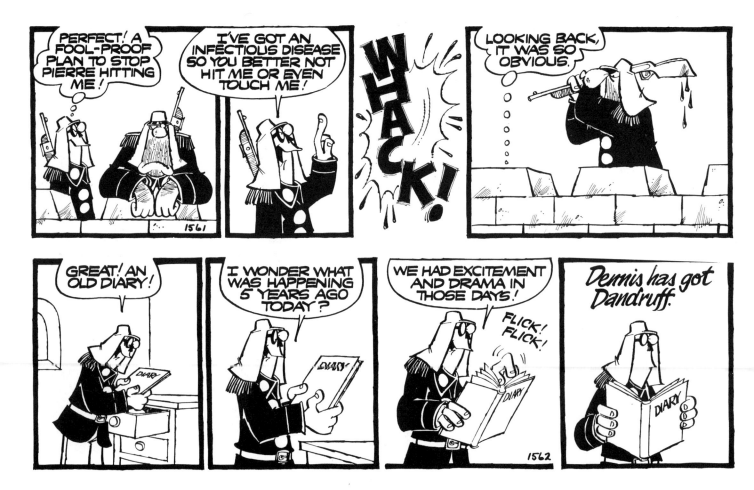

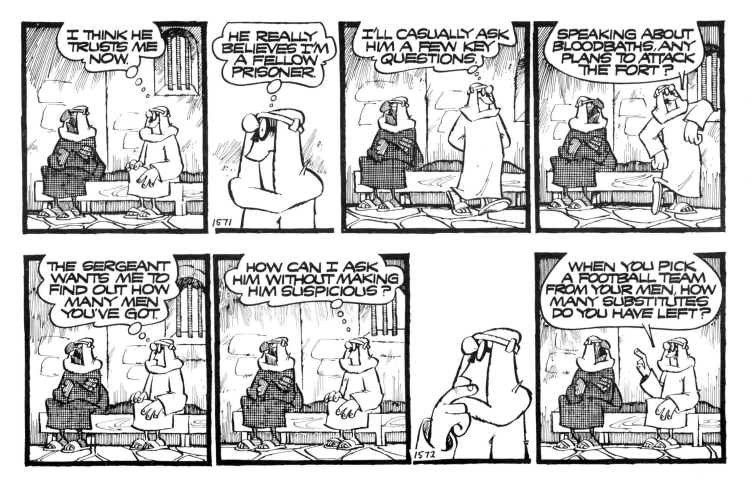

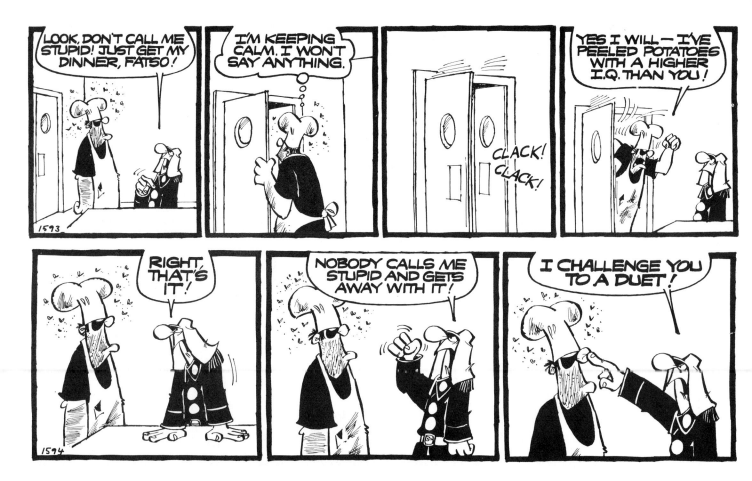

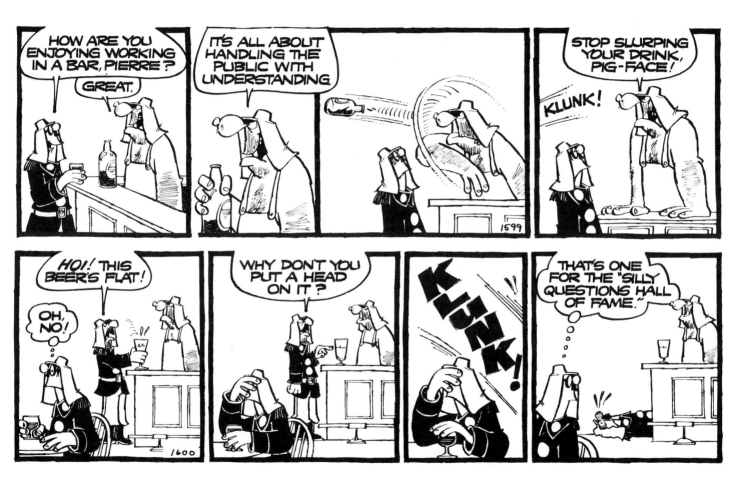

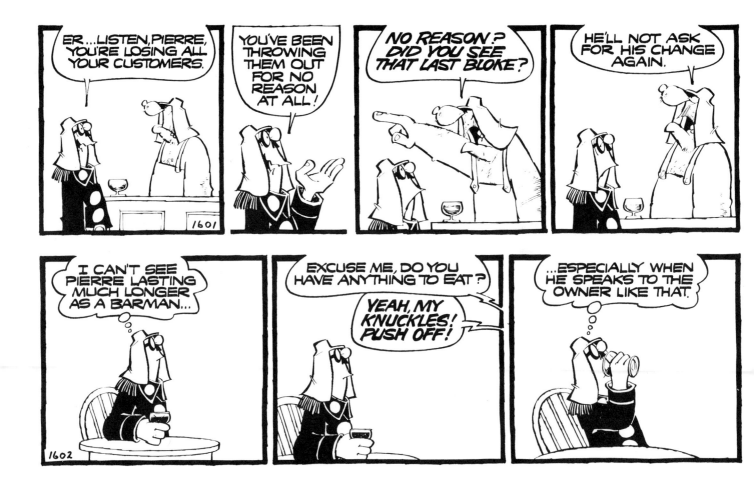

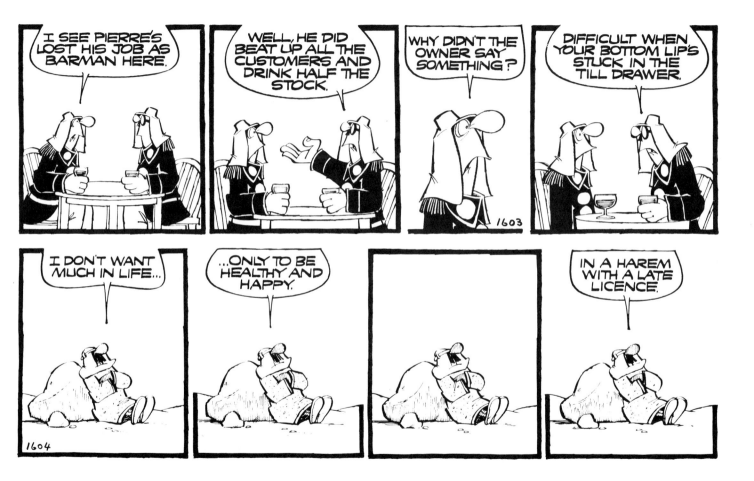

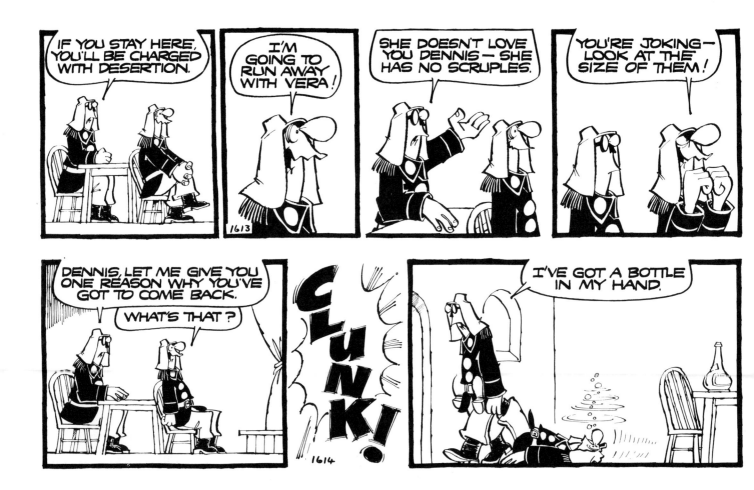

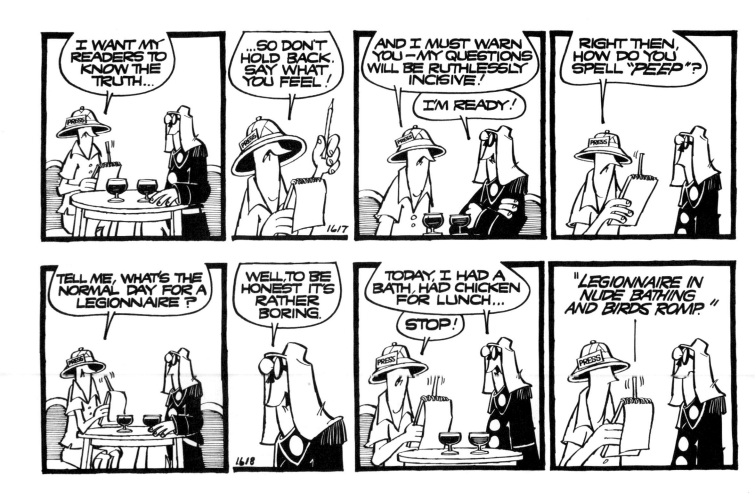

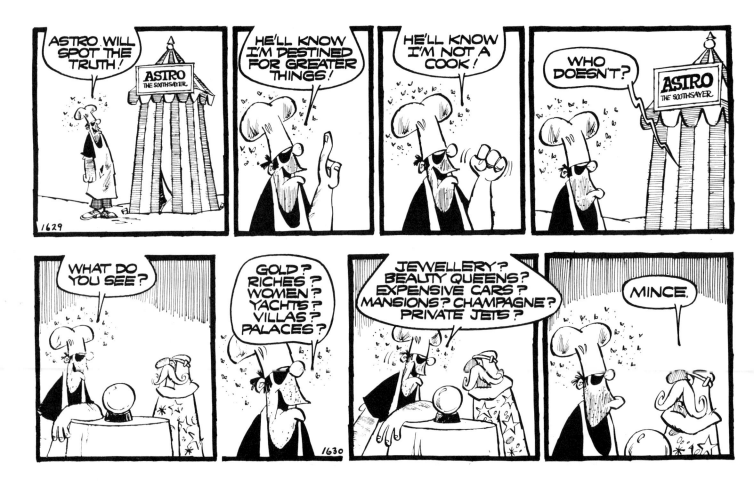

For further adventures of Legionnaire Beau Peep get

every morning

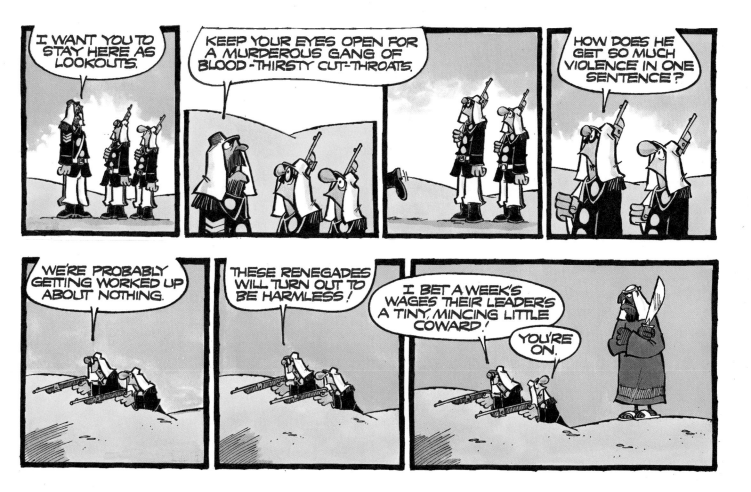